Sound at Sight

2nd series

Sight reading for Piano

Book 4

Grades 7 and 8

Published by
Trinity College London Press
trinitycollege.com

Registered in England
Company no. 09726123

Printed in England by Halstan, Amersham, Bucks.

Sound at Sight 2nd series

Playing or singing music that has not been seen before is a necessary part of any musician's life, and the exploration of a new piece should be an enjoyable and stimulating process.

Reading music requires two main things: first, the ability to grasp the meaning of music notation on the page, and second, the ability to convert sight into sound and perform the piece. This involves imagining the sound of the music before playing it. This in turn implies familiarity with intervals, chord shapes, rhythmic patterns and textures. The material in this series will help pianists to develop their skills and increase confidence.

This second series of *Sound at Sight* builds on the first, by adding a plethora of new exercises for each level. These newly composed pieces have been written by a variety of leading educational composers in a wide range of styles, realistically reflecting what students will encounter in their progressive study of the instrument. This in turn provides essential exam preparation.

Trinity's sight reading requirements are stepped progressively between Initial and Grade 8, with manageable increases in difficulty between each grade. Towards the end of each grade selection in this book, some exercises may be a little more challenging than the exam criteria, but attempts at these will ensure that candidates are amply prepared. Some tips on exam preparation are given at the back of this book, along with an at-a-glance table of the requirements at each level.

Contents

Trinity College London would like to thank Mike Cornick, Robin Hagues, Robert Ramskill and John York for their work on this series.

Grade 7

The keys of A♭ and E majors are introduced at this level, along with the new time signature of $\frac{9}{8}$. Pedalling is essential and any common terms for tempo should be expected. Trills may also be encountered.

1

2

3

4

5

6

8

10

12

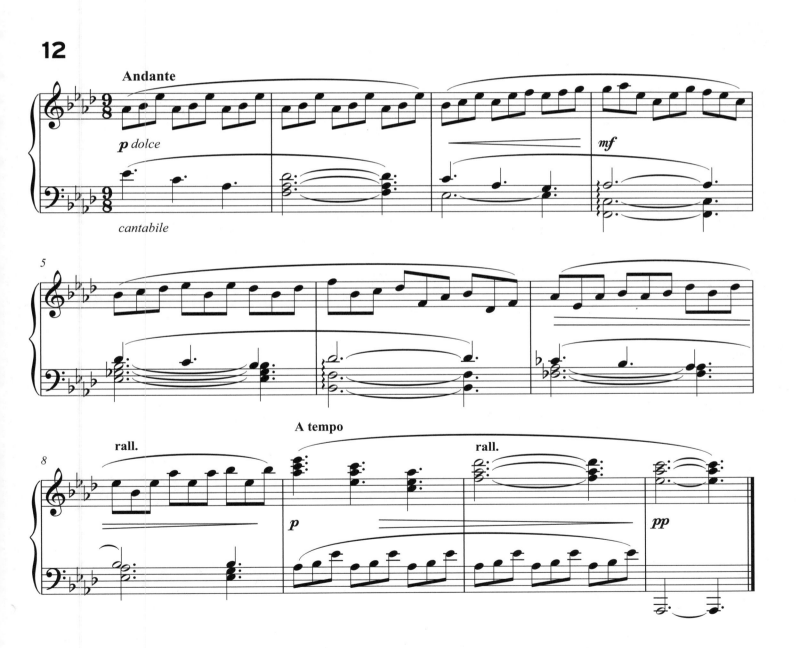

13

Allegro appassionato

14

Quite fast

15

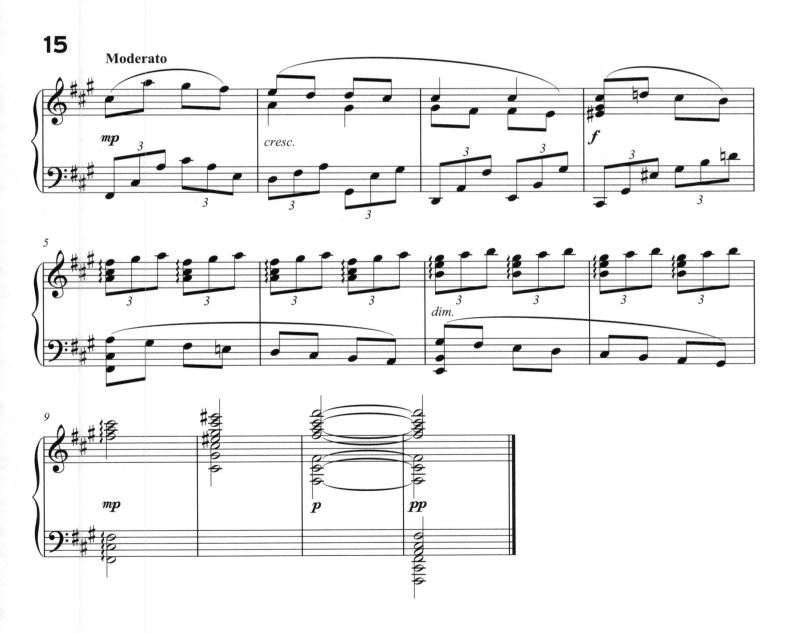

16

Allegretto ritmico

Grade 8

New key signatures at this level are B and D♭ majors, and G♯ and B♭ minors. Double sharps and double flats are now also present, along with the additional time signature of 2/2. Time signatures may also change within an exercise. Triplets and duplets are now included as are separate dynamics for each hand. Clef changes and the use of the *ottava* symbol may be seen. Any dynamic and tempo indications may be used.

1

2

Largo
Rubato con espress.

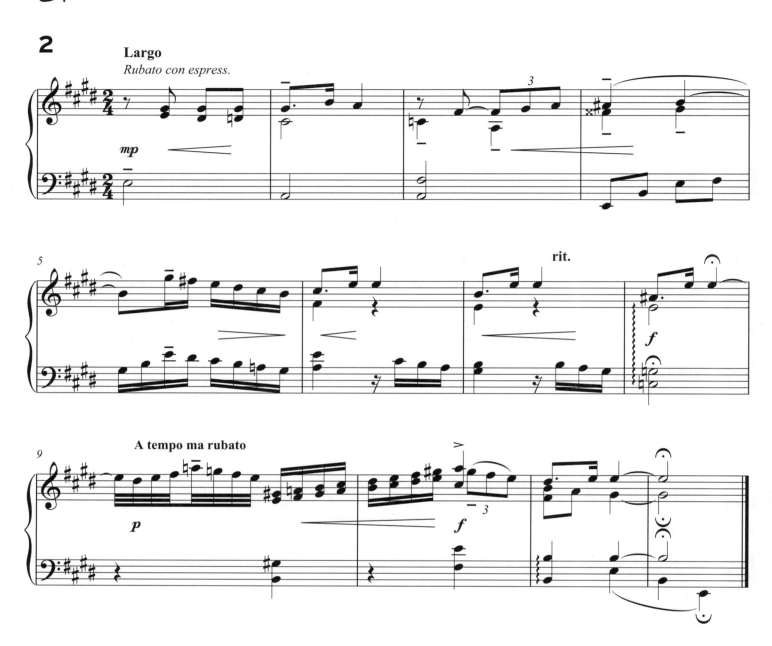

3

Largo

4

Allegro moderato (jazz style but with 'straight' quavers)

5

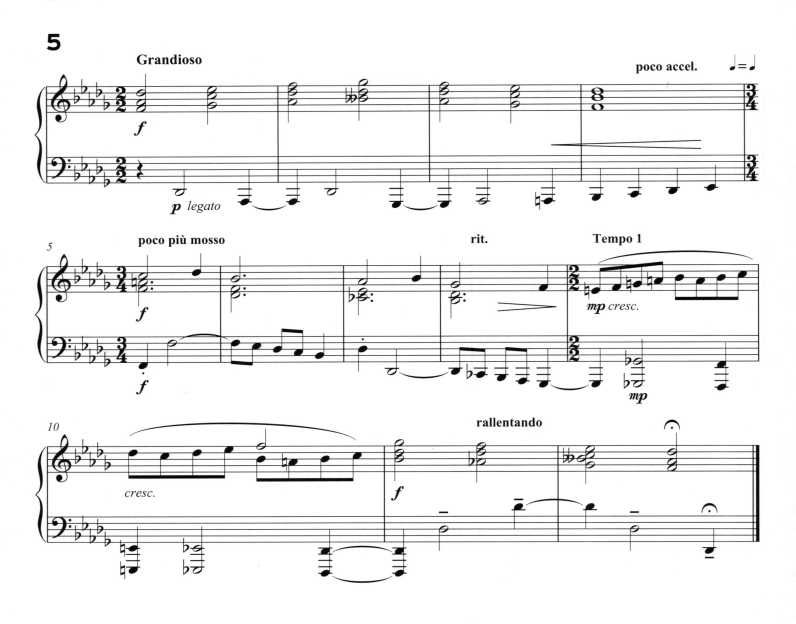

6

7

8

Larghetto

9

10

11

Allegro ma non troppo

12

13

Grazioso, non lento

14

Moderato – Tempo di Tango

15

16

17

Moderate blues tempo

Exam advice

In an exam, you have half a minute to prepare your performance. Use this time wisely:

- Check the key and time signature. You might want to remind yourself of the scale and arpeggio, checking for signs of major or minor first.

- Look for any accidentals, particularly when they apply to more than one note in the bar.

- Set the pace in your head and read through the piece, imagining the sound. It might help to sing part of the music or to clap or tap the rhythm. You can also try out any part of the test if you want to.

- Have you imagined the effect of the dynamics?

When the examiner asks you to play the piece, do not forget the pace you have set. Fluency is more important than anything else: make sure that you keep going whatever happens. If you make a little slip, do not go back and change it. Give a performance of the piece: if you can play the pieces in this book you will be well-prepared, so enjoy the opportunity to play another piece that you didn't know beforehand.

Sight reading requirements at a glance

The following table gives a general guide of the requirements pianists can expect to encounter at each level, and where they are encountered in this series of books. The complete detailed specifications can be found in the current syllabus. **Candidates should always refer to the requirements listed in the most recent syllabus when preparing for an exam.**

Sound at Sight 2nd Series	Grade	Keys*	Time signatures*	Note values*	Dynamics & tempi*	Articulation*
Book 1	Initial	C major	$\frac{2}{4}$	♩, ♩ and ◝	***p***, ***f*** and *moderato*	simple phrase marks
	Grade 1	G major; A minor (white notes only)	$\frac{4}{4}$	○	***mf*** (maximum of 2 different dynamics)	
	Grade 2	A minor (including G sharp)	$\frac{3}{4}$	♩. and ties	*allegretto*	
Book 2	Grade 3	D minor		♫ and ♪	***mp*** and *andante*	slurs
	Grade 4	D major; E minor		♪, ♪. and ♪	< >	*staccato* & accents
Book 3	Grade 5	F, B♭, E♭ & A major; B & G minor (inc. modulation to dominant/relative major)	$\frac{6}{8}$	♪., ♪ and ♪	*rit., rall., accel.* and *a tempo*	pause; simple pedalling
	Grade 6	F♯ & C minor				pedalling required but not always marked
Book 4	Grade 7	E & A♭ major	$\frac{9}{8}$		any common terms	pedalling essential
	Grade 8	B & D♭ major; G♯ & B♭ minor (inc. double sharps & flats)	$\frac{2}{2}$ & changing time signatures	duplets/ triplets	*cresc.* and *dim.* as text ***ff, pp*** change in terms; different dynamics for RH and LH	*tenuto*

* Please note that at any given grade, candidates are also expected to know the requirements of the preceding grade(s).